Jumping Up

CHARLES C. WALCUTT
GLENN McCRACKEN

Consultants:
LEILANI CAMARA
MARGARET R. EMERY
RICHARD C. HUNTER

Lippincott Basic Reading D

HARPER & ROW, Publishers   New York   Philadelphia   Hagerstown   San Francisco   London

1817

Acknowledgments

Grateful acknowledgment is made to the following authors and publishers to use copyright materials. Every effort has been made to obtain permission to use previously published material. Any errors or omissions are unintentional and the publisher will be grateful to learn of them.

"The Best Dream" an adaptation of a Native American legend from AND IT IS STILL THAT WAY, Legends told by Arizona Indian Children with notes by Byrd Baylor, copyright © 1976. By permission of Charles Scribner's Sons, Publishers.

"Somebody Stole Second" adapted from SOMEBODY STOLE SECOND by Louise Munro Foley. Copyright © 1972 by Louise Munro Foley. Reprinted by permission of Delacorte Press.

"The Snake That Sneezed" adapted by permission of G. P. Putnam's Sons from THE SNAKE THAT SNEEZED by Robert Leydenfrost. Copyright © 1970 by Robert Leydenfrost.

"Two of Everything" adapted from "Two of Everything" in THE TREASURE OF LI-PO by Alice Ritchie, copyright © 1949 by Harcourt Brace Jovanovich, Inc.; copyright © 1977 by M. T. Ritchie. Reprinted by permission of the publisher. Adapted and reprinted by permission of Miss M. T. Ritchie and The Hogarth-Press LTD. (Canadian rights)

"This Happy Day" from THE LITTLE HILL, copyright © 1949 by Harry Behn; copyright © 1977 by Alice L. Behn. Reprinted by permission of Harcourt Brace Jovanovich, Inc.

"The Magic Porridge Pot" from THE MAGIC PORRIDGE POT by Paul Galdone. Copyright © 1976 by the author and reprinted by permission of Houghton Mifflin/Clarion Books, New York.

"We're Off to See the Wizard," copyright © 1939, renewed 1967 Metro-Goldwyn-Mayer, Inc. All rights administered and controlled by Leo Feist, Inc. All rights reserved. Used by permission.

"Which Color is Cooler?" from CHILDREN'S PLAYMATE magazine, copyright © 1971 by Review Publishing Company, Inc., Indianapolis, Indiana. Adapted by permission of the publisher.

"Use Your Brain" an adaptation of the complete text of USE YOUR BRAIN by Paul Showers. Copyright © 1971 by Paul Showers. A Let's-Read-and-Find-Out Science Book. By permission of Thomas Y. Crowell, Publishers.

"By Myself" text of "By Myself" from HONEY, I LOVE AND OTHER POEMS by Eloise Greenfield. Copyright © 1978 by Eloise Greenfield. By permission of Thomas Y. Crowell, Publishers.

continued on page 218

Contents

To the Hills   1

Review Unit 1   4

Review Unit 2   8

Camp Fun   11

Marla's Adopted Pet   15

No Pickles   22

Review Unit 3   26

The Fox and the Stork   29

The Best Dream   33

Review Unit 4   37

A Line Can . . .   40

A Close Call   43

Review Unit 5   49

A Fair Share   51

Review Unit 6   56

Friends   60

Review Unit 7   64

At the Seashore   66

Review Unit 8   72

How *Jumping Up* Was Made   74

How to Make a Book Yourself   80

Review Unit 9	84
This Happy Day	86
Henny-Penny	87
Review Unit 10	98
The Snake That Sneezed	100
Review Unit 11	108
A Place for Dancing	110
The Magic Porridge Pot	116
Review Unit 12	124
City Snow, Country Snow	126
Somebody Stole Second	128
Review Unit 13	140
All Together Now	142
Which Color is Cooler?	148
Two of Everything	150
By Myself	161
Antique Toy Museum	162
Beauty and the Beast	173
The Story of Laura Bridgman	183
The Mechanical Man	193
We're Off to See the Wizard	202
Use Your Brain	204
Krin's Story	211

Developmental pages: oi, oy—page 160; ew, eau—page 172; aw, au—page 182; /f/ph, gh—page 191; /k/ch, /sh/ch—page 192; silent w, silent k—page 201.

To the Hills

The dragons took a summer trip.
They went up to the hills.
They had a tent, some pots and pans,
And lots and lots of frills, oh yes,
And lots and lots of frills.

They stuffed it all into the car.
They packed it all just so.
The dragons jammed into the car,
And Dad said, "Off we go, oh yes,
Off to the hills we go!"

Dad started up the dragon car,
But it jerked front and back.
A big, big bump made Dad stop fast.
Again they had to pack, oh dear!
Again they had to pack.

It was so dark and very late
When they got to the camp.
They had to set up in the dark,
For they forgot a lamp, oh dear!
For they forgot a lamp!

The tent was first to be set up.
It was so big and tall.
They ran inside to see, and then . . .
The tent fell on them all, oh no!
The tent fell on them all!

The dragons, sad, all went to bed,
Until they saw the sun.
And then they grinned big grins and said,
"A summer trip *is* fun, oh yes,
A summer trip is fun!"

Review Unit 1

aA	eE	iI	oO	uU
a	an	ant	and	add
	man	ran	damp	hand
e	end	egg	wet	pen
	ten	nest	spend	dress
i	in	is	did	sit
	grin	drip	trip	stiff
o	on	odd	not	hot
	pond	drop	stop	rod
u	us	up	sun	rug
	fun	drum	must	hunt

n	nap	net	run	tan
r	rest	rip	trap	trust
d	dad	dig	did	red
m	mad	mud	am	stem
p	pan	pet	map	pup
s	sad	sip	gas	pass
t	tin	top	set	mat
g	get	gum	rug	drag

up the steps

in the nest

on top

is Peg

1. The pup sits in the sun.
2. Pat rests on the grass.
3. The cat ran fast.

c	cap	camp	cross	picnic
h	him	hug	hit	hat
f	fog	fun	if	sniff
w	win	went	swim	twin
l	last	land	sled	help
b	big	bend	tub	rib
k	kit	kiss	ask	milk
ck	neck	sick	black	stuck

a red sled 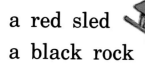   milk and eggs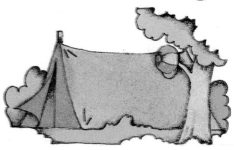
a black rock   a swim

1. Ben left his cap at camp.
2. Ask him to help us.
3. A big ant is on the bed.

nk	pink	wink	bank	sank
j	jam	jet	junk	jacks
v	van	vet	vest	visit
qu	quit	quick	quilt	squint
x	six	box	next	extra
y	yes	yet	yip	yank
z	zip	zap	quiz	buzz

an extra box 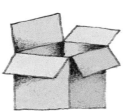 a pink vest

soft quilt   small jet

a big bank   the quick fox

1. You must zip up the jacket.
2. The van is black and tan.
3. Dick and his cat visit the vet.
4. Janet has six jacks.

Review Unit 2

ar

car	hard	yard	yarn
farm	start	scarf	garden

er

her	after	sister	summer
farmer	camper	fatter	bigger

ed

hunted	rested	started	handed
camped	asked	missed	tucked
hugged	planned	tipped	stepped

last summer   clapped her hands
asked her   ran after
planted a garden   started the car

aw

saw	paw	raw	draw
straw	dawn	yawn	lawn
fawn	hawk	claw	crawl

ow

owl	cow	now	how
down	town	clown	towel
brown	frown	drown	flower

will draw   soft towels

a brown owl   paw prints

into town   a big yawn

1. I saw a letter on her desk.
2. The clown jumped down the steps.
3. Jan has a brown straw hat.
4. A cat crawled under the bed.
5. How big is the hawk?

w with a and ar

wand	wander	want	swan
water	warn	warm	swarm

–ll

bell	fell	will	still
all	fall	tall	small
full	pull	bull	

–le

apple	bottle	nibble	puddle
uncle	pickle	simple	tumble

full of water   to the mall
jar of pickles   will pull

1. Uncle Lester stepped in a puddle.
2. They want six bottles of catsup.

10

Camp Fun

Ricardo and Dennis went to Camp Sunset on a big bus. They slept on bunk beds in log cabins.

Ricardo and Dennis unpacked in Cabin A. They got into swim trunks and went for a swim in the pond. Next they helped the rest of the kids in Cabin A hunt for frogs and bugs.

The campers in Cabin B planned a contest with Cabin C. The kids in Cabin C won the contest.

The kids in Cabin D helped Mr. Ladd fix a snack for all the campers.

Camp Sunset was fun for Ricardo, but he missed his pal Ted. Ricardo printed a letter.

Dear Mama and Papa,
Camp is fun. But I forgot
a mess kit
a blanket
extra socks
a net
mask and fins
a can of nuts
Ted.
XXX
Ricardo

"Ricardo, I left a big box in Cabin A," said Mr. Ladd. "It is for you."

Ricardo ran to his cabin to unpack the box. In it was the mess kit, the blanket, extra socks, the net, the mask and fins, a can of nuts, and . . . TED!

Ricardo hugged Ted. "If Dennis sees you, he will tell the kids," said Ricardo. "I must not let Dennis see you."

Ricardo jumped up onto his bunk. He tucked Ted under his blanket.

Dennis ran into the cabin. "Ricardo, I see a big bump in your bed," said Dennis. "Lift up the blanket. Let's see! Let's see!"

Ricardo held up Ted for Dennis to see.

"Come with me," said Dennis. He went up the ladder to his bunk. Ricardo went up after him.

"I see a big bump in *your* bed," said Ricardo. "Lift up the blanket."

Dennis held up his pal Fuzz. Dennis and Ricardo grinned.

"Pals are pals," said Ricardo. "I will not tell the kids if you will not tell."

"I will not tell," said Dennis.

The kids at Camp Sunset never did see Ted or Fuzz.

Marla's Adopted Pet

"Marla! Marla!" called Dad.

Marla jumped up and ran into the yard. Her mom ran after her. Marla saw Dad. He held a small fawn in his arms.

"I had to get the saw fixed in town," said Dad. "As I started into the woods, I stumbled upon a fawn. It was left in the grass."

"Can it stand up yet?" asked Marla.

"It is still too little," said Mom. "But I have a plan." Mom went back to the cabin.

Marla went to the far end of the barn. She fixed a warm bed in the straw for the fawn.

Mom ran into the barn and handed Marla a bottle. It was filled with warm milk. Marla sat down in the straw next to the little animal. She held the bottle as the fawn drank. It sucked and sucked on the bottle.

Marla petted the little spotted fawn. The fawn licked her hand. Marla rubbed its back and legs. The fawn started to stand up. Its legs wobbled and jerked, and the fawn fell back into the straw.

"Can it live on the farm with us?" begged Marla.

"A fawn is not a farm animal or a pet," said Mom. "A fawn must live in the woods."

"But it cannot stand up yet," said Marla. "It is too small to live in the woods."

Dad nodded. "Mom and I will let the fawn live on the farm until it gets bigger," he said.

"But you had better not get too fond of it," warned Mom.

But Marla *was* fond of the fawn. It was soft and had big brown eyes. Marla called the fawn Alvin.

A little after dawn, Marla fed Alvin.
He got bigger and bigger. Alvin tagged
after Marla as she fed the farm animals.
Alvin was *not* a big help. He ran after
the hens. He stepped in the egg basket.
He drank the water Marla got for
the pigs.

As Dad milked the cow, Alvin wanted to drink the milk. The cow kicked, the bucket tipped, and all the milk spilled in the straw.

Alvin got into Mom's garden. He pulled up plant after plant. He stepped in the flower beds. He nibbled on all the little melons and apples. Mom was mad at Alvin.

Alvin was a pest on the farm. But for Marla, it was the best summer she ever had. The summer went fast and Alvin got taller and fatter.

At the end of summer, Marla went to the barn. Alvin was not in his straw bed. Marla hunted in the yard. Alvin was not in the yard. Had he jumped into Mom's garden? Marla went from one part of the farm to the next.

"Alvin is lost," sobbed Marla. "I hunted for him in the barn, in the yard, and in Mom's garden."

"Alvin is not lost," said her dad.
"Alvin wants to live in the woods."

"But I want him to live with us," said
Marla.

"It is hard for you," said Mom. "But it
is best for Alvin to live in the woods."

"Will he come back?" asked Marla. "I
miss him."

"Alvin will not come back," said Dad.
"But he will never forget how you
helped him."

No Pickles

Scott Walters, his mom, and his sister, Jennifer, got up at six. Today they had to pack the rented van and move to Montana.

Scott and Jennifer packed box after box. Scott put tags on the boxes. Jennifer put the boxes into the van.

Mom called, "Did you pack Pickles?" (not the pickles you get in a jar, but Scott's little kitten, Pickles)

"No, I have not seen Pickles all day," said Scott. He jumped up and started to hunt for her.

22

"Pickles, Pickles!" called Scott. But
Pickles did not come. Scott hunted and
hunted. He hunted in the yard. He
hunted in all the closets and under the
steps, but still no Pickles!

"Mom, Jennifer," Scott called, "have
you seen Pickles?"

"No," said Mom.

"She is lost," said Scott.

"I will stop and help you hunt for
her," said Mom.

"Pickles can't be far," said Jennifer.

Mom, Scott, and Jennifer called and
called. They went up and down the
block. They hunted for Pickles all the
rest of the day.

At last Mom said, "We must get in the van now. Pickles will come back. I will ask the Baxters to keep her for us. We will come back for a visit and pick her up."

"No!" yelled Scott. "How can we move with no Pickles?"

Mom hugged Scott. "But we *must* go now," she said.

The Walters got into the van. Scott sat in the back, next to Jennifer. Mom started the van and off they went.

Scott felt sad. He wanted to have Pickles on his lap. He wanted to pet Pickles and have her lick his hand.

The van hit a big bump. All of a sudden, Scott saw the top of a box wiggle. Scott blinked and rubbed his eyes. The top of the box popped up. It was Pickles! Pickles was on top of the soft towels.

"Mom, Mom," yelled Scott, "it's Pickles!"

"She must have jumped into the box to have a nap," said Jennifer.

"I'm so glad to see you, Pickles," said Scott. "I missed you."

"So did I," said Mom. "After all, how can we ever get along with no Pickles?"

Review Unit 3

a—e

ate	cake	make	wake
safe	name	game	sale
late	plate	plane	skate

ai

tail	mail	pain	rain
wait	waist	trail	brain
train	paint	afraid	raisins

a box of raisins   a hard rain

a safe trip   pain in her arm

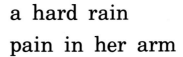

1. The mail was late.
2. Jane will go to the cake sale.
3. Did you have to wait for the train?

e

he   we   be   me

ee

see	bee	feet	week
feed	meet	beef	deep
sleep	steep	green	street
squeeze	queen	fifteen	between

feed the   a deep cut
a green tree   queen bee
down the street   a steep hill
on his feet   can squeeze

1. We will meet on Green Street.
2. I want to sleep on a soft bed.
3. He had beef for dinner.
4. I will be fifteen next week.
5. Lee will sit between us.

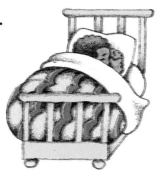

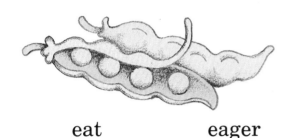

ea

eat	eager	tea	sea
seat	heat	neat	leaf
deal	meal	real	steal
treat	dream	feast	beast
lead	read	leap	clean
peas	peanuts	meat	beans

read to

peanut butter

bad dream

cup of tea

a hard seat

the green leaf

a meal of meat

the neat letter

can of beans

will speak to

1. Please sit down and read to me.
2. The heat made her feel weak.
3. Peanuts are a real treat.
4. Keep the desk neat and clean.
5. Can a seal swim in the sea?
6. We will eat raw peas from the garden.
7. Dean was eager to begin.

The Fox and the Stork

Fox was a clever animal. Fox liked to make fun of animals that were the least bit different.

"Stork seems odd to me," said Fox. "I will plan a trick and tease him."

"Please come to dinner," Fox said to Stork. "I will make a wonderful meal for us."

"I will be glad to come," said Stork.

Fox grinned as he began to fix the meal.

Stork came to eat dinner with Fox.

"M-m-m. It smells fantastic," said Stork.

"It is the best soup I have ever made," said Fox. "I am eager for you to taste it."

Fox put the soup on a flat plate. He put the plate between himself and Stork.

"Please eat, Stork," said Fox, as he lapped up the soup.

Stork pecked at the soup, but his beak just bumped the flat plate.

"Go on, Stork," said Fox, "help yourself." Fox grinned behind his paw as he ate and ate.

Stork pecked again. Bump! Bump! But Stork did not get one drop of soup.

Fox lapped it all up and smacked his lips.

"I will get even with Fox," Stork said to himself.

"Can you come to dinner next week?" he asked Fox.

"I'll be glad to come," said Fox.

Stork made a meal of beef and beans
for Fox. Stork put it in a tall jar with a
small neck. Stork set the jar between
himself and Fox.

"Please eat, Fox," said Stork.

Stork dipped his beak into the jar and
ate and ate.

Fox smelled the beef and beans. Stork
spilled a little bit on the grass. Fox
lapped it up.

"Go on, Fox," said Stork, "help
yourself."

Fox licked a little that stuck to the rim of the jar.

Stork grinned and gobbled up the last bit of beef.

Fox lost his temper. "I cannot eat from a tall jar!" he yelled. "You ate all the beef and beans. That was an awful trick!"

"Well," said Stork, "do not trick others if you do not want to be tricked yourself."

The Best Dream

A Native-American Tale

Coyote liked to trick other animals.
But other animals can plan tricks, too.

On the trail, Coyote, Porcupine, and
Skunk saw a meat wagon. The wagon
hit a bump, and a sack of meat fell off.
The animals ran to get it.

33

All the animals wanted the meat.

"Let's have a contest," said Coyote. "We will run down that steep hill. The winner can eat all the meat."

"Coyotes can run fast," Coyote said to himself. "I will win."

But Porcupine made himself into a neat little ball and tumbled down the hill. He passed Coyote and Skunk. Porcupine won the contest.

"Wait," said Coyote. "That is not fair. You did not run; you tumbled."

"Yes, let's have a different contest," said Skunk. "We will go to sleep. The animal that dreams the best dream can eat all the meat."

"Skunks are clever," said Skunk to herself. "I will have the best dream."

Coyote and Skunk settled down to take a nap. They went to sleep. But Porcupine was still awake. He had a plan.

After the nap, Coyote said what his dream was. Skunk did the same.

"Now tell us your dream, Porcupine," said Skunk. "Then, after that, we will name the winner."

"Well," said Porcupine, "I dreamed I ate the meat."

Coyote and Skunk leaped up. They ran to see if the meat was safe. But it was all gone.

Coyote and Skunk began to grumble. Porcupine grinned. "Well," he said, "I did have the best dream, didn't I?"

Review Unit 4

i

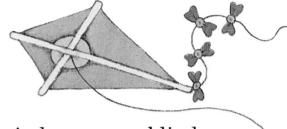

| I | find | mind | blind |
| pilot | silent | behind | remind |

i—e

| hide | ride | side | like |
| fire | tire | five | smile |

ie

| pie | tie | lie | die |
| dried | cried | tried | fried |

1. Tie the kite to the bike.
2. The pilot gave him a big smile.
3. "I tried to find her," cried Mike.

o

go	no	so	old
cold	hold	told	fold
sold	bold	gold	most

o — e

note	hole	hope	rope
home	bone	stone	alone
pole	broke	nose	rose

a deep hole

broke the rope

told me

fold the

sent a note

so cold

all alone

hold on to

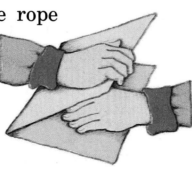

1. Her dog likes old bones.
2. Do not fall into the hole.
3. Mike sold five tickets.
4. I want to go to the park to see the roses.

oa

oak	oat	boat	coat
goat	soap	road	toad
moan	groan	float	toast

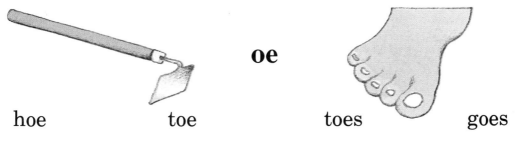

oe

hoe	toe	toes	goes

oak tree
bar of soap
ten toes
brown toad

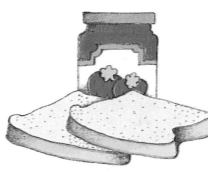

toast and jam
down the road
goes home
the boat floats

1. Joe saw a goat in a boat.
2. "I lost Dad's hoe," groaned Dick.
3. We went on a boat ride.
4. I like to eat oatmeal.
5. Jean can float on the water.
6. "Help me make toast," said Mom.

A Line Can . . .

A line can roll up like a hose
   or stick up like a nose.
It can stand up tall
   or wind into a ball.

A line can divide a road
   or become a fat toad.
It can be a tugboat
   or a warm winter coat.

A line can be a pail
  or a kite to sail.
It can be a small jet plane
  or a quiet lane.

A line can be a dial
  or a wide, wide smile.
It can make a game,
  a box, or your name.

41

A line can be a wave in the sea
  or a leaf on a tree.
Lines can make ribbons tied
  or potatoes fried.

Lines can make flames in a fire
  or an old, flat tire.
Lines can be a railroad track
  or dominoes in a stack.

A line can make a flower bend
  or even make this poem

A Close Call

A cold rain began to fall. It made little holes in the dust. Rose Olson leaned her bike on the old oak tree and ran inside. On the table was a brown paper bag. Rose peeked inside and saw the toaster. Beside the paper bag was a note.

Rose. Uncle Mike is in the hospital. Please go to Mrs. Reed's until I get back. Mom.

43

"I will get soaked if I go to the Reeds' now," said Rose. "I'll wait until the rain stops."

Rose started to make herself a snack. She got the toaster from the bag and plugged it in. She made toast and put peanut butter on it. Rose sat on the sofa in front of the TV to eat her snack. She was tired. Rose fell asleep as she waited for the rain to stop.

Rose woke up with a start. Smoke was
all over. "I must get help," she cried.
"I will run to get Mr. Reed."

As Rose ran down the steps, she saw
Mr. and Mrs. Reed.

"I saw smoke and called the fire
department," yelled Mr. Reed. "I am so
glad you are safe." Rose and the Reeds
waited in the road far from the fire.

The fire siren screamed as the fire truck arrived.

"Is Mrs. Olson inside?" yelled a fireman.

"No," replied Mrs. Reed. "Rose was home alone."

The firemen jumped down and ran to the fire. They had water hoses and foam. They were quick to get the fire under control.

All of a sudden, Rose was grabbed from behind. It was Mom at last. She hugged and kissed Rose. "I am so glad you are safe!" she said. "The fire truck passed me as I got off the bus. What happened?"

"I saw smoke," said Mr. Reed, "and I called the fire department. I started to run over to get Rose. But she ran down the steps to meet me."

"Were you inside?" asked Mrs. Olson.

"Yes," replied Rose. "I did not go to the Reeds'. I wanted to wait until the rain stopped, and I fell asleep."

A fireman came up. "The fire was not too bad," he said. "It seems to have started from a bad plug on a toaster."

"We do have a broken toaster," said Mrs. Olson. "But it was not plugged in."

"But it *was*," said Rose. "I wanted a snack, and so I plugged in the toaster. I am to blame for the fire."

"No, *I* am to blame," said her mom. "I was upset over Uncle Mike. I forgot to tell you the toaster was broken."

"Well," said the fireman, "it's all over now, and you are safe."

"You had a close call," he said to Rose. "But you were smart not to panic. Did your smoke alarm wake you up?"

"We do not have a smoke alarm," said Mrs. Olson, "but we will!"

Rose and her mom went to the Reeds' to relax. The next stop they made was at the market. They went home with a toaster *and* a smoke alarm!

Review Unit 5

are

care	dare	glare	stare
scare	spare	hardware	silverware

ir

sir	stir	girl	bird
dirt	first	twirl	skirt

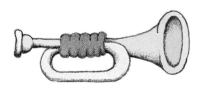 **or, ore**

or	for	horn	corn
more	wore	score	before

1. I have never seen him before.
2. Karen has dirt all over her skirt.
3. Did Joe go to the hardware store?

sh

ship	shop	she	shine
fish	dish	trash	finish

ch

chop	chip	chin	chore
bench	bunch	lunch	porch

–tch

catch	match	patch	scratch
pitch	ditch	stitch	switch

for his lunch   stitched the skirt
match the   finished the game

1. Do you like fish and chips?
2. Mom put a patch on Pam's shirt.
3. Is the green bench on the porch?

A Fair Share

Mr. and Mrs. Lord had a chain of stores in the West. They sold all kinds of shirts. From time to time, the Lords had to visit each store. Sometimes they had to be gone for a week or more. Then they asked Mrs. Dorando to come over until they got back.

Nora missed her mom and dad, but Mrs. Dorando was fun to be with.

"Let's go to the beach," begged Nora.

"OK," replied Mrs. Dorando, "but first we have some chores to finish."

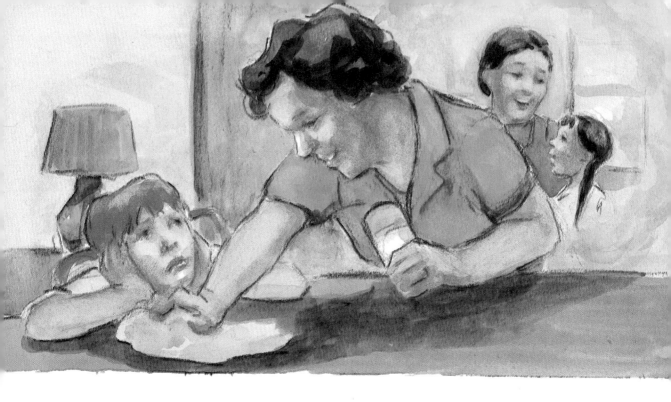

"Chores?" cried Nora. "Do we have to? I hate to do chores!"

"As a little girl," said Mrs. Dorando, "I felt just like you do. I hated to do chores. But each of us kids had to do a fair share. Mom told us how to make the chores into a game.

"After we finished, we had free time to do whatever we wanted. You and I can make the chores into a game, too. OK?"

"OK," said Nora. "Let's get started."

"I just did the wash," said Mrs. Dorando. "Let's see who can match more pairs of socks."

Nora matched six pairs. Mrs. Dorando matched nine.

"That's a score for me," said Mrs. Dorando.

"Now let's hang up the shirts, skirts, and pants. I wonder who will win this time?"

Nora was careful, but she still hung up more shirts, skirts, and pants than Mrs. Dorando.

"You win," said Mrs. Dorando. "Now the score is tied. I will go upstairs and patch the jeans you tore last week."

"You can take care of the kitchen. It will take time for me to find a needle and some pins. But I bet I finish first," she said.

Nora ran to the kitchen. She began to pull clean dishes, glasses, and cups from the dishwasher. She stacked them on the top shelf. Nora put the silverware into a drawer. Then she cleared the table and filled the dishwasher again. She flipped on the switch. At last the kitchen was clean and neat.

"I'm finished," she called. "Did I win?"

"Yes, you did," called Mrs. Dorando. "I'm not able to stitch fast, but your jeans are all mended. Now I have just one more chore for us to do."

"Please, no more chores!" groaned Nora.

"But it's a chore you will like," said Mrs. Dorando. "Let's see how fast we can pack a picnic lunch and get to the beach."

Nora smiled and reached up to get the picnic basket.

Review Unit 6

th

the	them	then	that
this	these	those	thin
thank	think	north	mother

 wh

whip	when	which	white
while	whale	wheat	wheel
whisper	whether	what	where

what is	third grade
his brother	whisper to

1. Thelma's father fixed her bike wheel.
2. Which is the biggest whale?
3. When will winter be over?

–ng

wing	sing	sang	song
hang	hung	ring	rang
rung	long	along	king
bring	thing	swing	string
spring	sting	stung	strong

sang a song   a strong wind

ring the   a bee sting

in the swing   will bring it

a thin string   hung up

1. Where is the string for the kite?
2. The bee stung James on his neck.
3. Spring begins in March.
4. You can come along with me.
5. The king wore a crown.
6. He sang a long song.
7. Which bird broke its wing?
8. Let's swing for a while.

–ing

sing	bend	jump	think
singing	bending	jumping	thinking
ringing	sending	bumping	sinking
swinging	lending	thumping	drinking

meet	sail	heat	toast
meeting	sailing	heating	toasting
greeting	mailing	treating	roasting

feeling	teaching	painting	reading
meaning	cleaning	sleeping	speaking

feeling fine   heating the water
teaching math   jumping over
printing your name   sending a note

1. We are thinking of going sailing.
2. Mrs. Singer was teaching us
   to make puppets.
3. The ship was sinking fast.

| get | shop | sit | run |
| getting | shopping | sitting | running |

swimming	tugging	dragging	sledding
whizzing	winning	stopping	fanning
dripping	planning	hopping	hugging

| make | hope | smile | joke |
| making | hoping | smiling | joking |

hiding	saving	poking	chasing
shining	waving	shaking	driving
waking	riding	taking	skating

whizzing downhill   chasing the ball
hiding eggs   dripping wet

1. Don is planning to bring me back home.
2. Will you be riding on the bus?
3. Kate's team is winning the game.
4. The twins went shopping at the store.
5. Mr. Sharp was telling jokes and smiling.

Friends

Running, jumping, tumbling, hopping,
Skipping, swimming in the sun.
Riding, diving, biking, sliding,
With a friend it's all more fun.

When you're itching and you're scratching,
Eyes and nose and throat all red,
Friends will come and entertain you;
Read to you while you're in bed.

Sitting down to eat your lunch,
Seeing what each other's got,
She gives you a bunch of sweet grapes.
You give her an apricot.

You ask him to get his train cars,
He will set them up with care.
He asks you to trade your marbles,
Friends are fair and so, you share.

Hitting, running to the bases,
You fall down and scrape your shin.
When your friend helps you feel better,
You yell, "Thank you" with a grin.

Smiling, calling, whispering, giggling,
Sharing secrets, jokes, and dreams.
Friends like being with each other,
Stick together like a team.

Friends can sit and chat and chuckle,
Just be still and think or read.
Friends are those you feel at home with.
Friends are something we all need.

Review Unit 7

–ed

land	print	lift	rent
landed	printed	lifted	rented
handed	hinted	shifted	dented
wait	roast	treat	need
waited	roasted	treated	needed
painted	toasted	seated	greeted
fish	match	block	rush
fished	matched	blocked	rushed
wished	scratched	rocked	brushed

matched the socks   treated me

wished on a star   roasted hot dogs

1. After dinner we fished in the pond.
2. Nate watched and waited for me.
3. Dean washed and brushed his hair.
4. The king was seated on his throne.

rope	like	rake	joke
roped	liked	raked	joked
hoped	hiked	baked	poked

wave	smile	care	fire
waved	smiled	cared	fired
saved	filed	shared	tired

asked	picked	stopped	ripped
camped	packed	slipped	dropped

called	yelled	planned	begged
smelled	warned	grinned	stirred

ripped her shirt   filed her nails
waved at me   saved his life
so tired   dropped a dime

1. He shopped and packed for his trip.
2. Sharon slipped and dropped the glass.
3. The teacher yelled and warned us.
4. We picked and shared the apples.

At the Seashore

Jason King and his mom visited the seashore for a long weekend. They met Mrs. White and her two children, Ethel and Marsha. All five of them liked the seashore. They also liked each other and became friends.

The kids had fun on the beach together. The two mothers chatted with each other as they watched the children.

"I think I'll catch a big fish," said
Jason. "We can roast it for lunch." He
cast his fishing line into the waves.

Marsha and Ethel ran to get their
fishing poles, too. They waded into the
water and cast their lines into the
waves. But the fish were not biting.

When the children didn't catch fish,
the mothers tried to think of something
to cheer them up.

"I have an idea!" cried Mrs. King.
"You can dig for clams. Then we can all
have clams for lunch."

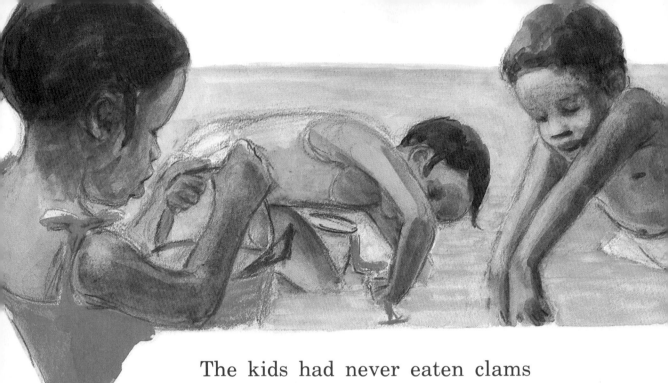

The kids had never eaten clams
before. They were eager to find some.
They rushed back to the cabin to get
buckets and shovels. Then the children
jumped into the water and began to
hunt. They dug and dug. At last they
felt big clams under the sand. They
filled a bucket with two dozen clams.
Marsha handed the bucket of clams to
her mother.

"Now what will we do with them?"
she asked.

"First, we must wash the clams," said
Mrs. White. "Go get some water."

The kids washed the clams to get rid of the sand. Then Mrs. White opened a clam with a short, sharp blade.

When the children saw the raw clam inside the shell, they cried, "We're not eating clams! Yuk!"

"I bet you will like them better when they are roasted," said Mrs. King.

The children gathered sticks and little logs that had washed up on the beach. They started a small fire. Then they put a grill over the fire and put the clams on top of it. Before long the clams sizzled, bubbled, and opened up.

The mothers put a clam on a paper plate for each child. Before Ethel tasted hers, she said, "This clam is too hot!"

Jason said, "This clam is too wet!"

Marsha licked her clam, and then smiled and gobbled it up. "It's not bad at all," she said. "If you taste one, I bet you'll like it."

Ethel and Jason each tasted a clam.

"This tastes OK," said Jason.

But Ethel grabbed her throat and said, "Yuk! Is this all we get to eat?"

"Let's see what we can find," said Mrs. King. "Come back to the cabin with me, Ethel. I planned a treat that we can all share."

Mrs. King and Ethel came back with a big picnic basket. It was filled with hot dogs, rolls, baked beans, grapes, and other things to eat.

Mrs. King put the pan of hot dogs and baked beans in the middle of the grill.

She put five rolls next to the pan. The rolls toasted a golden brown.

The feast smelled wonderful! The kids clapped and cheered. Then they lined up with their plates.

Mrs. King, Mrs. White, Marsha, and Jason filled their plates with baked beans, hot dogs, and hot roasted clams. Ethel did not put clams on her plate— just baked beans, hot dogs, and dessert.

"The next time we come to the beach, Dad will help me catch a big fish," boasted Jason. "We can roast *it* for lunch."

"OK," said Mrs. White, "but I'm still going to bring a picnic basket, just in case!"

Review Unit 8

ir

shirt	birth	chirp	chirped
first	thirst	third	thirteen

or

word	work	world	worse
worst	favor	flavor	color
doctor	sailor	editor	illustrator

the third girl   to the doctor
hard work   the first time
the worst dream   a favor

1. Which flavor do you like best?
2. Can you hear the birds chirp?
3. Herb's sister is an illustrator.
4. "I want to see the world," she said.

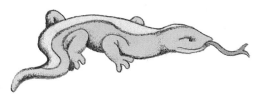

ar

wizard	lizard	backward	forward
dollar	collar	beggar	caterpillar

ur

fur	purr	burn	hurt
curl	curb	turn	turtle
nurse	purse	surprise	hamburger

a little lizard	turned up his collar
the cat's purr	sat on the curb
surprise visit	backward and forward
fur mittens	hurt her leg

1. Did you see *The Wizard of Oz?*
2. She gave her purse to the nurse.
3. The turtle went backward and forward.
4. I spent a dollar for lunch.
5. A caterpillar is like a worm.
6. Be careful not to burn the hamburgers.

How **Jumping Up** Was Made

Did you ever wonder how a reading book is made? It takes a long time and a lot of people to put together a reader. Here are just some of the steps it takes and some of the people that helped to make the book you have in your hands.

First the author and the editor planned what to put in the book. Then the author sat down and wrote stories he felt were fun for you to read. That was hard to do. The stories had to be made up of words that you are able to read. The author mailed his stories to the editor.

The editor worked on the stories. She checked all the words, the punctuation, and the spelling to see that they were correct. The editor also made sure the stories were not too long or too short. The editor worked with the author to make each story as interesting as possible.

The editor also had to go to the library. She looked for poems and stories printed in library books. You can find their names under *Acknowledgments* near the front of your book.

When all the stories had been
collected, the editor sent them to the
compositor. The stories came back
printed on long strips of paper. The
editor checked them to see if any
mistakes had been made.

Next the art director asked her
assistant to cut the long strips apart
and to paste the stories into pages.

Then the art director gave the stories
to illustrators. She asked the illustrators
to draw pictures in pencil to go with
each story. When the pictures were OK,
the illustrators finished them in color.
The art director chose the picture that
was to go on the cover.

When all the pages were finished and each picture was in place, the pages were sent to the printer. Pictures were taken of the finished pages. These were put on a large printing press. Printed pages came out folded in the correct order.

Next the covers and the binding were put on each book.

The finished books were shipped to a place to be stored until orders began to arrive. When your order came in, your books were shipped to you.

Now you have some idea of the number of people and the hard work it takes to make a reader like *Jumping Up*.

How to Make a Book Yourself

Here's how to make a book for yourself. You can be the author, the editor, and even the illustrator.
To make your book you will need:

- 1 sheet of colored paper for the cover
- 5 sheets of plain paper, the same size or a little smaller than the cover
- 2 feet (60 cm) of yarn or string
- paper punch
- pair of scissors

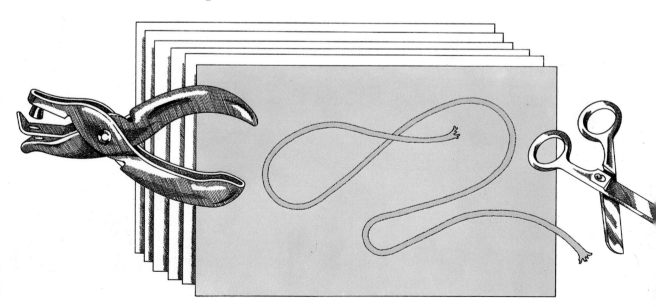

1. Fold each sheet of paper and the cover down the middle.

2. Open up the 5 sheets of paper and put one on top of the other. Open up the cover and put it under the pages.

3. Ask someone to hold the sheets of paper and the cover for you to keep them from slipping while you punch two holes. Punch the first hole one inch (2.54 cm) from the top of the paper. Punch the second hole one inch (2.54 cm) from the bottom of the paper.

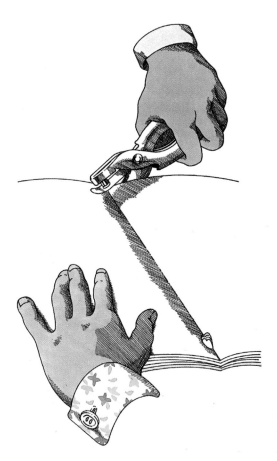

4. Working from the inside of your book, put the string or yarn in one hole. Put the other end of the string or yarn in the other hole. Pull both ends until the string or yarn is even, and then tie them together.

5. Before you think of a title or a name for your book, plan what you will put in it. It is up to you what things go into your book. Your book can be about *you*, the things you like to do or eat. It can be about your mother, father, brothers, sisters, and pets. Your book can also be about a trip or something you did last summer.

6. Now think of a title for your book. Print it on the cover. Draw or cut a picture from a magazine to put on the cover.

7. The first page of your book is called the *title* page. The title of your book goes on this page, too. Under the title, print your name as the author or person who made up the book.

8. Number each page near the bottom.

9. Now you can fill the pages with your ideas. Draw or cut pictures from a magazine to illustrate what you wrote.

It is your book and you are its author, editor, and illustrator!

Review Unit 9

−ay

may	way	say	pay
play	stay	spray	away
maybe	today	yesterday	birthday

−y

by	my	dry	cry
why	shy	fly	try

is shy   ran away

will dry the   today is

1. Yesterday was Ray's birthday.
2. Do you want to try to fly a kite?
3. May I stay inside today?
4. Which way do you turn to go home?
5. Maybe we can go to the play.

–y

baby	lady	lazy	very
every	happy	bumpy	dirty
party	worry	hurry	hungry

–ly

sadly softly quickly suddenly

–ey

key turkey valley monkey

very hungry	baby monkey
ran quickly	every month
hurry up the	dirty glass

1. Is the baby hungry yet?
2. That is a very lazy donkey.
3. Shirley was happy to play with us.
4. Terry ran quickly up the steps.

This Happy Day

Every morning when the sun
Comes smiling up on everyone,
It's lots of fun
To say good morning to the sun.
   Good morning, Sun!

Every evening after play
When the sun goes away,
It's nice to say,
Thank you for this happy day,
   This happy day!

Harry Behn

Henny-Penny

A Play

Narrator 1: One day Henny-Penny was picking up corn in the barnyard when—*whack!*—something hit her on the head.

Henny-Penny: Oh my! The sky is falling. I must go and tell the king.

Narrator 2: So she went along, and she went along, and she went along, till she met Cocky-Locky.

Cocky-Locky: Where are you going, Henny-Penny?

Henny Penny: Oh, I'm going to tell the king the sky is falling.

Cocky-Locky: May I come with you?

Henny-Penny: Yes, you may.

Narrator 3: So Henny-Penny and Cocky-Locky went to tell the king the sky was falling. They went along, and they went along, and they went along, till they met Ducky-Lucky.

Ducky-Lucky: Where are you going Henny-Penny and Cocky-Locky?

Henny-Penny:
Cocky-Locky: } Oh, we're going to tell the king the sky is falling.

Ducky-Lucky: May I come with you?

Henny-Penny:
Cocky-Locky: } Yes, you may.

Narrator 1: So Henny-Penny, Cocky-Locky, and Ducky-Lucky went to tell the king the sky was falling. They went along, and they went along, and they went along, till they met Goosey-Loosey.

Goosey-Loosey: Where are you going, Henny-Penny, Cocky-Locky, and Ducky-Lucky?

Henny-Penny:
Cocky-Locky:
Ducky-Lucky:
} Oh, we're going to tell the king the sky is falling.

Goosey-Loosey: May I come with you?

Henny-Penny:
Cocky-Locky:
Ducky-Lucky:
} Yes, you may.

Narrator 2: So Henny-Penny, Cocky-Locky, Ducky-Lucky, and Goosey-Loosey went to tell the king the sky was falling. They went along, and they went along, and they went along, till they met Turkey-Lurkey.

Turkey-Lurkey: Where are you going, Henny-Penny, Cocky-Locky, Ducky-Lucky, and Goosey-Loosey?

Henny-Penny:
Cocky-Locky:
Ducky-Lucky:
Goosey-Loosey:
} Oh, we're going to tell the king the sky is falling.

Turkey-Lurkey: May I come with you?

Henny-Penny:
Cocky-Locky:
Ducky-Lucky:
Goosey-Loosey: } Yes, you may.

Narrator 3: So Henny-Penny, Cocky-Locky, Ducky-Lucky, Goosey-Loosey, and Turkey-Lurkey all went to tell the king the sky was falling. They went along, and went along, and went along, until they met Foxy-Loxy.

Foxy-Loxy: Where are you going,
Henny-Penny, Cocky-Locky,
Ducky-Lucky, Goosey-Loosey, and
Turkey-Lurkey?

Henny-Penny:
Cocky-Locky:
Ducky-Lucky: } Oh, we're going to tell
Goosey-Loosey: the king the sky is
Turkey-Lurkey: falling.

Foxy-Loxy: But this is such a long way
to the king. There is another, much
shorter way. Do you want me to
lead you?

Henny-Penny: ⎫
Cocky-Locky: ⎪
Ducky-Lucky: ⎬ Oh yes. Please do.
Goosey-Loosey: ⎪
Turkey-Lurkey: ⎭

Narrator 1: So they went along, and
they went along, and they went along,
until they came to a dark hole on the
side of a hill. Now this was Foxy-
Loxy's cave. Foxy-Loxy said to Henny-
Penny, Cocky-Locky, Ducky-Lucky,
Goosey-Loosey, and Turkey-Lurkey—

Foxy-Loxy: This is the short way to the
king. We will be there in no time. I
will go in first, and you can come
after me, one by one.

Henny-Penny:
Cocky-Locky:
Ducky-Lucky:⎫ Splendid idea! Fine!
Goosey-Loosey:⎭ Why not?
Turkey-Lurkey:

Narrator 2: So Foxy-Loxy quickly went
into his cave, but he didn't go very
far. Foxy-Loxy was hungry.

He turned and waited for Henny-
Penny, Cocky-Locky, Ducky-Lucky,
Goosey-Loosey, and Turkey-Lurkey.
Turkey-Lurkey was the first to go into
the dark hole that led to the cave. He
didn't go far when Foxy-Loxy snapped
off his head.

Narrator 3: Then Goosey-Loosey went in.
Snap! Off went her head.

Narrator 1: Then Ducky-Lucky waddled
down. Snap! Off went Ducky-Lucky's
head.

Narrator 2: Then Cocky-Locky marched into the hole. He hadn't gone far when Foxy-Loxy went snap!

Narrator 3: But Cocky-Locky had time to warn Henny-Penny. He called to her to save herself. She turned and off she ran home.

Narrators 1, 2, 3: So Henny-Penny never did get to tell the king the sky was falling.

Review Unit 10

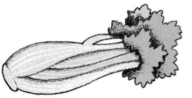

soft c

cent	center	celery	celebrate
ice	nice	face	race
dance	fence	once	twice

city	circus	circle	cider
pencil	decide	excited	medicine

icy	fancy	lacy	mercy

once or twice   a lacy shirt

icy water   the old city

circus tent   square dance

1. How did you decide to celebrate?
2. My mother's office is in Center City.
3. Lance put two pencils in his desk.
4. I had celery sticks for lunch.
5. Did the doctor give you medicine?

 **soft g**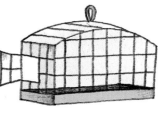

gentle	germ	age	cage
page	damage	package	change
large	strange	giant	gigantic
giraffe	magic	dingy	stingy

 **–dge**

edge	ledge	hedge	bridge
badge	fudge	budge	judge

in the cage   edge of the page
damage the   under the bridge
on the ledge   gentle giraffe

1. My uncle Roger can do magic tricks.
2. I need exact change for the bus.
3. His badge was large and shiny.
4. Marge made fudge for the contest.
5. The cave was dark and dingy.

The Snake That Sneezed

Once upon a time, in a lovely forest, a little snake named Harold lived with his mother and father. The time came when Harold decided to leave home and seek his fortune.

"Get plenty to eat," his mother said.

"But don't bite off more than you can chew," his father added.

With this advice, Harold said farewell and crawled away.

Later Harold met a white, furry
animal.

"Hello, what are you?" Harold asked.

"I'm a rabbit," he said.

"Well, I'm a snake," said Harold, and
remembering his mother's advice, he
swallowed him up. Then he crawled on
to seek his fortune.

A short crawl later, Harold met a colorful bird.

"Hello, what are you?" Harold asked.

"I'm a peacock," she said.

"Well, I'm a snake," said Harold, and he swallowed her up. Then he crawled on to seek his fortune.

Then Harold saw a very, very tall animal.

"Hello, what are you?" Harold asked.

"I'm a giraffe," she whispered gently from far above.

"Well, I'm a snake," said Harold, and he swallowed her up.

By this time, Harold had a strange
feeling in his tummy, but he crawled on.
He saw an animal with a hairy mane
and a tassel on his tail.

"Hello, what are you?" asked Harold.

"I'm a lion," he roared.

"Well, I'm a snake," said Harold, and
he swallowed him up.

Harold felt so full he was hardly able to budge, but he crawled on. He saw an animal with two bumpy humps on his back.

"Hello, what are you?" Harold asked.

"I'm a camel," he said.

"Well . . . I'm . . . a . . . snake," Harold said, and with much difficulty he swallowed him up.

Harold felt like curling up someplace and going to sleep. Harold crawled down a path. The path led to a large orange tent. Harold crawled to the edge of it. He was staring into the eyes of a tiny, tiny bug. The bug quickly hopped on Harold's nose.

"Please . . . get off my nose!" Harold hissed. "I think I'm going to sn . . . sn . . . sn . . . SNEEZE!"

When the sawdust had finally settled,
all the animals he had swallowed up
were inside the orange circus tent.

The man who ran the circus was very
pleased to have the animals in his
circus. He even made Harold the star of
the center ring.

"At last I have made my fortune,"
said Harold. "But never again will I bite
off more than I can chew."

Review Unit 11

–sion

permission   expression   admission
decision   occasion   television

–tion   10 + 2 = 12

action   station   vacation
lotion   attention   position
addition   celebration   definition

big celebration   on television
gas station   a hard decision

1. My family is going on a vacation.
2. I have an invitation to her party.
3. Admission to the circus is a dollar.
4. Did you get permission to go?
5. Please pay attention.

short oo

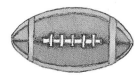

look	took	book	cook
foot	good	wood	stood
football	crooked	cookbook	bookstore

long oo

too	zoo	moon	noon
boot	food	soon	cool
pool	room	spoon	smooth

too soon	at the moon
swimming pool	a loose tooth
good food	a cool room

1. Did you get that balloon at the zoo?
2. My father is a good cook.
3. I'll meet you in the lunchroom at noon.
4. Roberto took us to a football game.
5. The wooden desk feels smooth.
6. Can the baby eat food with a spoon?

A Place for Dancing

Onawa lived in a small town with a thick forest on all sides. She and her parents were Native Americans.

In the evening by the fireplace, her father told of Indian life long ago. In those days there were no television sets or gas stations. Indians rode horses in the wind and camped in the forest. They danced in celebrations under the moon. Onawa loved to hear these tales.

But not all of the tales were so happy.
Some told of animals that came snooping
after dark and wolves that ran in packs.
Onawa paid little attention to these
scary tales, for she liked the happy ones
far better.

One day she said to herself, "Father's
tales are exciting. I want to dance in
the forest. I want to camp under the
stars as Indians did long ago."

Onawa made a decision. "I will go to the forest. I will camp and dance in the forest just like in the old days."

After dinner she packed a bag with a blanket and some food. Then she made her way quietly into the street. After hiking for quite some time, she reached the edge of town.

There stood the forest. It looked dark and lonely. Branches moved in the wind like long arms. Suddenly Onawa did not feel brave anymore.

"But I have come all this way,"
she said with a gulp. "I can't turn
back now."

Onawa went in among the dark pine
trees. She laid her blanket on the soft
pine needles and sat down.

The moon and stars were above her in
the sky. "This is a perfect place for
dancing," she said. "Just like in a story
father told."

Onawa stood up and began to dance.
Suddenly something in the bushes
behind her moved. It seemed to be
coming closer and closer.

She remembered her father's scary
tales—the ones she did not like. Goose
bumps popped up on her skin. Maybe
it wasn't a perfect place for dancing,
after all!

She scooped up her blanket and bag
and ran all the way home. When she
got to the door, her father was waiting
for her. He had an angry expression on
his face.

"Onawa, who gave you permission to be away after dark? Where have you been? I want an explanation!"

"I just wanted to sleep in the forest," said Onawa. "I wanted to dance under the moon like the Indians in the old days. I forgot the scary tales you told."

Her father hugged her.

"Maybe now you will remember them all—the happy ones *and* the scary ones," he said. "Next time, we'll go to the forest together."

The Magic Porridge Pot

Once upon a time, a little girl and her mother lived in a cottage in a small village. They were very poor and had nothing to eat.

One day the little girl went into the woods near the cottage to hunt for food. She hunted for a long time, but she was not able to find anything. The little girl sat on a tree stump and started to cry.

116

"There is no food for Mother and me. What will we do? We are so hungry."

"Do not worry, my dear," someone said. "You will never be hungry again."

The little girl looked up with a surprised expression on her face. An old woman was standing in front of her. The woman was leaning on a crooked stick and had a small black pot in her hand.

The old woman handed her the pot. "This is a magic pot, my dear," said the old woman. "Put it on the fire, then say, 'Cook, Little Pot, cook!' At once the pot will fill up with thick, sweet porridge. When you have had all you can eat, you must say to it, 'Stop, Little Pot, stop!' Then the magic pot will stop cooking."

"Oh, thank you so much," cried the little girl.

"Never forget the magic words, my dear," said the old woman and she disappeared.

The little girl rushed home to give the pot to her mother.

"This is a magic pot that will cook porridge," the little girl explained. "An old woman in the woods gave it to me."

The little girl set the magic pot on the fire. Then she said, "Cook, Little Pot, cook!" Thick, sweet porridge bubbled up from the pot, just as the old woman had told her. Then the little girl said, "Stop, Little Pot, stop!" And the magic pot stopped cooking.

Now the little girl and her mother had as much porridge to eat as they wanted. They were very happy.

One afternoon the little girl asked her mother for permission to visit a friend. The friend lived at the other end of the village. After the little girl left, her mother began to get hungry. So she set the magic pot on the fire and said, "Cook, Little Pot, cook!" The pot cooked some porridge, and the mother ate until she was full.

Soon the porridge bubbled to the top of the pot. The mother tried to stop it, but she had forgotten the magic words! The pot became too full, and the porridge began to spill over the edge.

"Halt, Little Pot, halt!" she cried.

The porridge only cooked and bubbled
over faster and faster.

"No more, Little Pot, no more!" cried
the mother, as the porridge covered
the floor.

The mother struggled to the door and
opened it wide. She ran into the street,
and so did the porridge.

"Quit, Little Pot, quit!" screamed the mother, as she ran to get her little girl.

The mother finally reached the cottage where the little girl was visiting. The porridge was not far behind.

"Help, help," she called. "Come home. The pot keeps cooking and cooking."

When the little girl reached the cottage she cried, "Stop, Little Pot, stop! Stop, Little Pot, stop!" And the magic pot stopped cooking.

Everyone in the village ran into the street with dippers, spoons, cups, buckets, pans, and pitchers. They dipped up the porridge, they scooped up the porridge, and they spooned up the porridge. It was like a celebration. Everyone feasted for days and days.

After that, no one in the village ever went hungry again. And the little girl and her mother never forgot the magic words: "Stop, Little Pot, stop!"

Review Unit 12

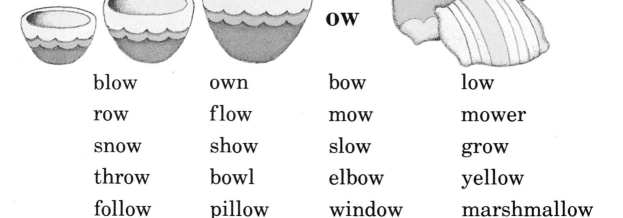

ow

blow	own	bow	low
row	flow	mow	mower
snow	show	slow	grow
throw	bowl	elbow	yellow
follow	pillow	window	marshmallow

a yellow pillow
faster or slower
a dirty window
a pet show

will grow
a low stool
will not follow
a bowl of ice cream

1. He fell in the snow and hurt his elbow.
2. Vicky sat in the first row at the show.
3. Please tie a yellow bow on this package.
4. My cat sleeps on a pillow in the window.
5. Carlos will mow the lawn every week.
6. May we toast marshmallows over the fire?

ou

out	our	about	shout
loud	house	sound	found
four	fourth	pour	court
you	youth	soup	group
your	yours	tour	tourist
young	touch	trouble	country

found a quarter   a lot of trouble
four days ago   in the country

1. The four young men shouted for help.
2. Our dog is scared of loud sounds.
3. Please pour some soup in each bowl.
4. Your group may go out first.

City Snow, Country Snow

Snow falls on the city.
With a touch of its fingers,
It makes patterns on
Cars, and houses, and skyscrapers.
Whirling, twirling,
It draws white pictures
On streets and playgrounds.

126

Snow falls on the country.
It weaves a row on branches,
Then doubles back and
Weaves another row.
Dancing, prancing,
It shapes fluffy animals
In forests and farmyards.

Snow falls.
And in city and country,
Children make
   Snowballs,
   Snowmen,
   Snowangels,
And are glad there's
   Snowschool!

Peg Chagnon

Somebody Stole Second

"It's GONE!" Pete yelled. He stopped running. Scooter stopped throwing. And Jeff ran in from third base.

It *was* gone! Second base had disappeared.

"Fine thing," said Pete. Pete was a member of the Jets. "First time this year that I hit a double and when I get here, second base is gone."

"Somebody stole second!" yelled
Scooter, as he jumped up and down with
his hand over his mouth. "Somebody
stole second!" He poked Pete in the ribs.
"Just like the Giants," yelled Scooter.
"Somebody stole second!"

"BE QUIET, SCOOTER!" yelled Pete.
"When the Giants steal second, it's
GOOD. THIS . . . IS BAD."

"Yes," said Jeff, slowly. "Somebody
really stole second. They came along and
carted it away."

Pete, Scooter, and Jeff stared at the
ground where second base had been.

"Well, we still have first," said Jeff.
He was looking over at the yellow towel
that was first base.

"And THIRD!" yelled Scooter. He ran
down to check the old patch of green
carpet.

"But NO SECOND," said Pete.

Second base was an old red and black
car cushion. Or at least, it was before
it disappeared.

Pete's mother used to sit on it when
she was driving the car.

One day Pete's father got another car
cushion, so they put the old cushion in
Abner's doghouse.

Abner was Pete's dog. He was a funny
dog. He didn't like dog food. He liked
cherry vanilla ice cream. He didn't like
dog treats. He liked marshmallows and
crackers with butter and honey.

And he didn't like doghouses. He liked
Pete's bedroom.

So, when the Jets needed a second
base, Pete took Abner's red and black
car cushion.

Abner never slept in the doghouse anyway. He slept on a mat in Pete's bedroom until Pete's mother turned off the lamp next to the bed.

THEN . . . Abner jumped into bed with Pete. Pete had a nice soft bed with a nice big pillow.

Every morning Abner jumped out of Pete's bed. He lay down on his mat just before Pete's mother came to wake them up.

Since Abner had Pete's bed to sleep in, he didn't really need the doghouse or the car cushion.

And that was how the car cushion became second base.

Scooter sat down in the dirt. "How can we play the Stars without a second base?" he asked.

The Stars and the Jets had a big game coming up the next day. It was a play-off.

"We're in trouble," said Pete. "We can't play without second base."

"We have to find it," said Jeff.

"Well, it didn't get up and run away," said Scooter. "Somebody STOLE it."

"Wait a minute!" said Jeff. "Who's our enemy?"

"The Stars!" shouted Pete.

"Let's go," yelled Jeff.

The Jets went looking for the Stars. The Stars were practicing for the big game.

"Keep your eyes open and follow me," whispered Pete. "Maybe we'll spot it."

The Stars were a good group. They had four players. They had two catcher's mitts. And they had a second base. But it wasn't the Jets' red and black car cushion. It was a dirty old potato sack.

"I don't see it," said Pete. "Let's go."

They spent all day looking for second
base. They asked a lot of kids. They
looked in a lot of funny places—the
garage, the washer, the dryer, and the
baby's sandbox.

But they did not find second base.
They looked for a long time. Then Pete
had another idea.

"Maybe," he said, "just MAYBE . . .
Abner borrowed his pillow back."

They ran out and looked in the
doghouse. It was dark inside. Pete
crawled in. It was smelly. "It's dark in
here," he yelled. He sounded funny.
"Nope!" Pete shouted. "No second base!"
He backed out of Abner's doghouse.

"No second base . . . no play-off
tomorrow," said Scooter sadly.

"I'm tired of looking," said Jeff.

"Me, too," said Pete. "Let's go inside."

136

They went upstairs to Pete's bedroom
to read.

Pete and Jeff flopped on the floor.
Scooter flopped on the bed. He wiggled.
He squirmed. He rolled around. Then he
looked at Pete and said, "You have a
lumpy bed."

"I have a nice bed!" shouted Pete,
crossly.

"Lumpy!" yelled Scooter. He pounded
the bed with his fist. "There's a big
lump here!"

Pete was mad. He got up to look. His bed *was* lumpy. "I've never seen that lump before." He yanked down the blanket.

"It's second base!" he yelled. "We found it." They all looked. There it was—second base—in the middle of Pete's bed.

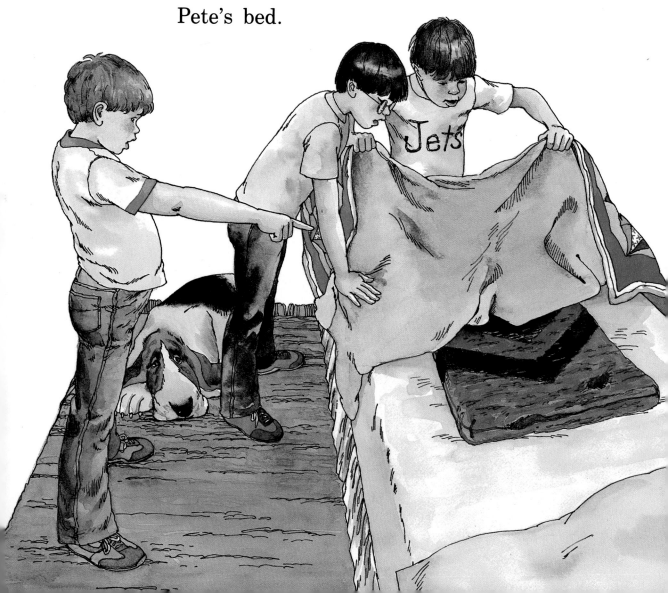

"ABNER DID IT!" yelled Pete. "Abner
wanted his own pillow! That silly dog!"
Pete was grinning. They were all
grinning. "This is going TOO far!" yelled
Pete. "He can eat my cherry vanilla ice
cream. He can eat my marshmallows
and crackers. He can sleep in my room.
BUT . . . he'll just have to find another
pillow. NOBODY, not even ABNER, gets
away with stealing second base from
the Jets!"

Review Unit 13

u

unit	usual	uniform	united
music	museum	bugle	tuna
flu	student	super	truth

u — e

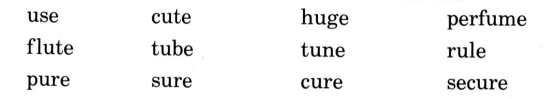

use	cute	huge	perfume
flute	tube	tune	rule
pure	sure	cure	secure

white uniform   had the flu

music student   Mom's perfume

1. My sister can use this costume.
2. Have they found a cure for the flu?
3. You have to play by the rules.

ue

due	rescue	blue	clue
glue	true	argue	Tuesday

ui

suit	fruit	juice	juicy
bruise	cruise	suitcase	fruitcake

a bowl of fruit

a blue suit

on a cruise

orange juice

next Tuesday

a bruise on my leg

had no clue

rescue unit

1. Can you glue this vase together?
2. Is this a true story?
3. Let's not argue about it.
4. These books are due at the library.
5. Have you seen the Statue of Liberty?
6. He put the fruitcake in his suitcase.

All Together Now

Florence played flute in the band.
Tom played tuba. Bruce played bugle.
They practiced making music every day
after school.

But Florence did not like the tuba.
"It is too loud and deep," she said to
herself, "just like a huge, croaking toad.
The tuba sounds so ugly next to my
sweet flute."

Tom did not like the bugle. It had
such a strong, pure sound. It was like a
horn in a king's palace. "I wish my horn
sounded like that," Tom said to himself.
"The bugle makes my tuba sound old
and grumpy."

And Bruce did not like the flute. It
was so very sweet, like the sound of
birds singing. And the flute had more
solos than his bugle. "Florence is a
show-off," he grumbled.

One day Tom did not come to band
practice. He was sick at home with
the flu.

"Good," said Florence. "Now, that
stupid, croaking tuba is gone."

The band played, but the music did
not sound the same. Florence hated to
admit it, but she missed Tom and his
tuba. "Without the tuba," she said to
herself, "the band has no deep notes.
Even a croaking toad adds some music."

The next day Bruce had the flu. He stayed home in bed.

"Good," said Tom. "The strong bugle is gone. Now my tuba will not seem old and grumpy."

The band played a tune, but it did not sound the same. Tom hated to admit it, but he missed Bruce and the bugle. Without them, the band was weak.

On the third day, Florence stayed
home with the flu.

"Good," said Bruce. "Now that show-off
Florence cannot steal the show. I will
get the solo today."

The band played several tunes, but it
was not the same. Bruce hated to admit
it, but he missed the sweet sound of
the flute. "I miss the sound of birds
singing," he said to himself.

The next day no one was sick. The band members put on blue uniforms and began to warm up. The tuba made deep oom-pahs. The flute sang like a bird. The bugle was strong and pure.

The band leader raised her arm. "All together now," she said.

The band played. Florence, Tom, and Bruce nodded at each other. Today the music sounded better than usual.

Which Color Is Cooler?

You will need:

  ice cubes

  2 small bowls of the same size

  a black cloth to cover one bowl

  a white cloth to cover the other bowl

Directions:

Put the same number and size of ice cubes in each bowl. Cover one bowl with the black cloth and the other with the white cloth. Put the bowls in the sun for 30 minutes.

Uncover the bowls and compare the melting cubes. Which color cloth made the ice melt faster—the white or the black?

The black cloth held the heat from the sun and melted the ice cubes. The white cloth bounced most of the sun's rays back into the air.

White clothes are popular on hot summer days. Can you figure out why this is true?

Two of Everything

A Chinese Folk Tale

One day Mr. Hak-Tak found a big brass pot. He was sure there must be some use for it. Mr. Hak-Tak decided to take the pot home with him.

As he was going along, his wallet fell to the ground. To make sure he did not lose it, he placed his wallet inside the big brass pot.

When he got home, Mrs. Hak-Tak asked, "What do you have there?"

"I found this pot," replied Mr. Hak-Tak. "It's too big to cook in and too small to take a bath in. But maybe we can use it for something."

Mrs. Hak-Tak stooped over the pot to look inside. As she bent down, her hairpin fell into the pot. She reached in to get the hairpin and Mr. Hak-Tak's wallet. Suddenly she cried out.

"What is it?" her husband asked.

Mrs. Hak-Tak said, "It must be magic!
I reached into the pot to get my hairpin
and your wallet, and look at this. Now
there are two hairpins and two wallets!
Both of them are exactly alike."

"Open the wallets," said Mr. Hak-Tak.
"One of them must be empty."

But both wallets held the same
amount of money. Now the Hak-Taks
had twice as much money as they had
that morning.

"Put in the old yellow blanket and see what happens," said Mr. Hak-Tak. "We need another blanket for winter." Mrs. Hak-Tak pulled out two yellow blankets.

Then Mrs. Hak-Tak said, "Let's put our money in again and again. We will take out more money each time. Soon we'll have so much money, we will be able to get everything we need."

They dropped the money from one wallet into the pot and pulled out twice as much. Then they added that money to the money in the other wallet and dropped all of it in. After a while, the floor was covered with money.

The next morning Mr. Hak-Tak went shopping to get all the things they needed. While he was gone, Mrs. Hak-Tak sat on the floor and put her arms around the pot.

"My dear pot," she said, "you are the best friend we have ever had."

She stood up and bent over to look inside the pot. Just then, her husband pushed the door open and came in. Mrs. Hak-Tak turned around a little too quickly and fell into the pot!

Mr. Hak-Tak rushed over and pulled her out by the ankles. Then he saw the kicking legs of another Mrs. Hak-Tak in the pot! He pulled her out, too. Now a second Mrs. Hak-Tak stood beside them.

"I will not have a second Mrs. Hak-Tak in the house!" screamed the first Mrs. Hak-Tak. She cried and stormed about.

"One wife is all I want," said Mr. Hak-Tak. "But I had to pull her out of the pot!"

"Put her back in!" cried the first Mrs. Hak-Tak.

"What? And take out two more?" cried her husband. "Oh, no! If two wives are too many for me, what will I do with three?" Then he stepped back, tripped, and fell into the pot!

Each Mrs. Hak-Tak grabbed an ankle
and pulled him out. Then they saw
another pair of kicking legs in the pot!
Soon a second Mr. Hak-Tak, exactly like
the first, stood beside them.

The first Mr. Hak-Tak did not like the idea of his double any more than the first Mrs. Hak-Tak had liked the idea of her double. He stormed and raged about.

Then the first Mrs. Hak-Tak had a very clever idea. "It is good that now there is another one of you, as well as another one of me," she said. "That couple can live next door to us. Then you and I can live by ourselves again."

And that is what they did. The first Hak-Taks made themselves a fine house with money from the pot.

Then they made one just like it next door for the other couple.

The villagers were very surprised at how rich the Hak-Taks had become. They were even more surprised at the couple who looked just like the Hak-Taks. Everyone said, "It looks like the Hak-Taks decided to have two of everything, even themselves."

oi

oil	boil	soil	foil
broil	spoil	voice	choice
coin	join	joint	point
noise	noisy	moist	moisture

oy

boy	toy	joy	enjoy
annoy	loyal	royal	oyster

By Myself

When I'm by myself
And I close my eyes
I'm a twin
I'm a dimple in a chin
I'm a room full of toys
I'm a squeaky noise
I'm a gospel song
I'm a gong
I'm a leaf turning red
I'm a loaf of brown bread
I'm a whatever I want to be
An anything I care to be
And when I open my eyes
What I care to be
Is me

Eloise Greenfield

Antique Toy Museum

Many people like to collect things. Some people collect stamps. Some people collect coins. Some people collect old things. Very old things are called *antiques*.

For hundreds of years, boys and girls have played with toys. Today some people collect antique toys. They may display them at home for their friends to see.

If the collection is large and valuable, they may loan it to a museum. That way many people can come to see and enjoy the toys. One man's collection became so large that he started his own museum.

In 1969 Mr. Leon Perelman decided to put his unusual collection of three thousand antique toys on display. He fixed up an old house as a museum.

Today many tourists, girl and boy scouts, and classes of children come to visit the Perelman Antique Toy Museum.

The museum employs three people who keep the museum going. The *curator* is in charge. The curator takes each group of people on a tour of the museum. The toys are kept in glass cases so they will not get soiled or damaged. Sometimes the curator will take the toys out of their cases to show people how they work.

The *cataloguer* keeps a record of all of the toys. The cataloguer can tell you how long each toy has been in the museum and how it happened to get there.

The *custodian* takes care of the museum. The custodian keeps it neat and clean.

In the museum are cases and cases of toys. These toys were enjoyed by children long ago. On the first floor of the museum are different kinds of games. There are also many toy soldiers standing in rows. Some are made of wood and some of tin. Some point their muskets, and others load cannons.

There is an entire case of noisy toys, such as cap pistols and exploders. All of them are about one hundred years old.

There are even cases of circus wagons. Each wagon has a little animal in a cage. The wagons are pulled by toy

horses. On some wagons are the words
Royal Circus. The wagons are made of
metal and the colors are faded now. But
you can imagine children long ago
playing circus. You can almost hear
them yelling in a loud voice, "Hurry,
hurry. Come and see the Royal Circus."

Upstairs at the museum the walls are
lined with cases containing cars, trucks,
trains, and trolleys. Ride back in time.

Take your choice from old-fashioned cars, taxicabs, buses, trucks, trolleys pulled by horses, and of course, trains. There are engines, boxcars, and a caboose from a hundred years ago. You can almost hear a child's voice from the past saying, "All Aboard."

The top floor of the museum is the most popular. It contains the toy banks.

All the banks are made of metal. They
have parts that move when coins are
dropped into them. Drop a coin in one
and a boy scout raises a flag. Drop a
coin in a camera bank and a picture
pops up. For a penny, a dog will do a
trick or a girl will jump rope.

The oldest toy in the museum is a doll. It was made in 1740. There are both baby dolls and grown-up dolls. Some are made of china and some of wood. One doll has a face that can change from happy to sad.

Perhaps you can visit an antique toy
museum yourself some day. Do you
think the toys you play with now will
ever become antiques?

ew

new	few	dew	chew
grew	flew	drew	crew
stew	blew	threw	screw

eau

beauty   beautiful

Beauty and the Beast

Once upon a time there was a young girl named Beauty. Beauty lived with her father and her two sisters in a little house on the edge of the forest.

Beauty and her family were poor. They had to work hard, but they were happy all the same. They enjoyed living together in their little house near the forest.

One day Beauty's father was hunting in the forest. He came upon a huge castle. The garden was full of beautiful roses covered with dew.

Beauty's father remembered that Beauty loved roses. He looked for the castle gardener. He wanted to ask if he could pick a few roses for Beauty.

Beauty's father did not find the gardener. He did not see anyone at all. So he picked one rose, and off he went down the path.

Suddenly there was an awful noise. Beauty's father saw a huge beast standing before him. The beast was very angry. He grabbed the rose from Beauty's father and threw it on the ground.

"Old man," he growled, "you will be sorry you picked my rose. You have spoiled my rosebush. Now I will make you my prisoner."

"I'm very sorry," said Beauty's father. "I only wanted a rose for Beauty, my youngest girl. If you keep me prisoner, there will be no one at home to care for my family. I cannot stay here."

"I will let you go," growled the beast,
"if you send Beauty to take your place."

When he reached home, Beauty's
father told the story to his children.
Beauty was afraid, but she said, "You
are needed here to care for the family.
I will take your place, Father."

"No, Beauty, I cannot let you go," said
her father.

"But I *must* go," replied Beauty. "I
will not allow my father to become the
prisoner of any beast!"

176

When Beauty reached the castle, the beast welcomed her. Beauty was afraid of him, but she tried to be polite. She tried not to stare at the beast. He was ugly. The beast had fuzzy hair all over his body and long, yellow teeth. He had sharp claws and a deep, gruff voice. But his eyes were sad.

As the beast showed Beauty to her room, he growled, "Beauty, will you marry me?"

"No, Beast," said Beauty. "I cannot marry you." The beast's eyes grew even sadder.

The next day Beauty discovered that
the castle was a wonderful place. When
Beauty was hungry, food arrived,
including her favorite stew. When
Beauty wanted to read, the best books
hopped off the library shelves. When it
got dark, the candles lit themselves.
And in the mornings, beautiful new
clothes flew from the closet for Beauty
to put on.

Every day Beauty enjoyed herself. And every evening the beast asked Beauty to marry him. Beauty always said no.

The beast was good to Beauty. When he saw that Beauty missed her family, he let her go home to visit them.

"But you must come back in two weeks," growled the beast. "If you do not come back then, I will surely die."

Beauty enjoyed her visit with her family. She told them all about the beast and his wonderful castle.

Beauty discovered that she missed the beast. She remembered how sad he looked.

Beauty's family begged her to stay longer. Beauty stayed a few extra days, and then she returned to the castle.

Beauty did not see the beast anywhere. At last she found him in the garden. The beast was lying very still. His eyes were closed.

"What have I done!" cried Beauty. "Oh, Beast, please do not die. I am sorry I stayed away so long. I love you. I want to marry you."

The beast slowly opened his eyes.
Beauty was so happy. She gave the
beast a big hug and a kiss.

Suddenly the beast changed into a
handsome prince!

"You have broken the evil spell," said
the prince. "I am so grateful to you. At
last I am myself again."

Beauty agreed to marry the prince.
The prince was good and kind like the
beast. And now, when Beauty looked
into his eyes, she saw that they were no
longer sad. They were happy.

aw

awful	awning	raw	saw
law	jaw	paw	claw
yawn	fawn	lawn	dawn
hawk	straw	crawl	shawl

au

pause	cause	because	caution
sauce	saucer	sausage	haunt
haul	fault	somersault	

182

The Story of Laura Bridgman

One August evening a little girl ran home for supper. The girl's name was Laura Bridgman. The year was 1836. Laura was seven years old, and she lived on a farm.

How Laura wished she could tell her mother about her day! Laura had held a baby hawk. The hawk had a fuzzy body and very sharp claws.

But Laura had no way to tell her mother about the hawk. Laura Bridgman could not speak.

When Laura was a baby she was very sick. When she got better, she could not see, hear, smell, or taste. And because Laura could not hear words, she could not speak to people. But Laura did have her sense of touch. She had to "hear" and "see" with her fingers, her hands, and the rest of her body.

Laura liked to help around the farm. She fed the animals and helped to put down fresh straw for them to sleep on. She also helped her mother set the table, cook, and make clothes.

Mr. Asa Tenney lived near Laura's farm. Laura liked to visit him. She helped him care for his baby hawk and other animals.

One day Laura went to visit Mr. Tenney. She wanted to feed the little hawk. Where was it?

The little hawk had grown up and flown away. But Mr. Tenney had no way to explain that to Laura. So Laura did not understand what had happened. She cried and threw her shawl down. She stamped her feet.

Laura needed a way to speak to others. And she needed a way to find out what others wanted to say to her. If only Laura's clever hands could "speak" and "hear" for her!

A teacher named Dr. Samuel Howe worked with blind children. He showed them how to read with their hands. They traced their fingers over raised letters.

People who cannot hear can form letters and words with their hands. In this way they can "speak to" and "hear" other people.

Dr. Howe wanted to teach Laura. Mr. and Mrs. Bridgman sent Laura to study with Dr. Howe in Boston. Because no one could tell Laura why she had to leave home, Laura was confused. Why was she in this strange place?

Dr. Howe showed Laura how to "read" the raised metal letters. A teacher named Miss Drew showed Laura how to form letters and words with her hands.

At last Laura had a way to tell people what she wanted to say. Soon she was asking many questions. She began to read books. She discovered how to print. She sent letters to her family and to Mr. Tenney.

Laura showed other students how to make letters with their hands. Then they were able to speak to her by "spelling" into her hand.

Newspapers printed articles about Laura and all the things she could do. Many people came to visit her. They

saw her read, make shawls, do math,
and teach other children.

One visitor was an author from
England named Charles Dickens. Mr.
Dickens told of his visit with Laura in a
book called *American Notes*. The mother
of a girl named Helen Keller saw this
book. Like Laura, Helen had an awful
illness when she was a young child. And
like Laura, Helen could not speak, see,
or hear.

Helen Keller's mother sent a letter to the place where Dr. Howe worked. "I want my Helen to find the magic of Laura Bridgman," Mrs. Keller told Dr. Howe. "I want her to be able to speak to others and to understand them."

Helen Keller did do these things. She even visited Laura in Boston. When Helen Keller grew up, she became an author. In her book she told about Laura Bridgman, the first person to "see," "speak," and "hear" with her hands.

USA 15¢

HELEN KELLER
ANNE SULLIVAN

ph

photo   photograph   phone   telephone

phrase   pharmacy   alphabet   elephant

nephew   orphan   autograph   microphone

gh

laugh   laughter

ch

chorus	chrome	character	chemistry
school	echo	ache	anchor
mechanic	mechanical	orchestra	stomach

ch

Chicago	chute	parachute	chef
machine	machinery		

192

The Mechanical Man

Phillip was a young boy who enjoyed making mechanical toys. One day Phillip was very excited. That day his class was going to the Space Center. His teacher had shown the class photographs of a mechanical man at the Space Center.

Phillip and his best friend Joseph were eager to meet Mechanical Max. Before they looked at anything else in the Space Center, the boys went to find him. They hoped to get his autograph.

193

"I wish the mechanical man lived at my house," said Joseph. "Just think— Joseph Andrew Boyd, the only kid on the block with a mechanical man to do his chores! Wow!"

"Look, there he is," yelled Phillip. "He's coming up to meet us. I want to touch him and see what he is made of."

"He seems to be made of shiny chrome," said Joseph. "And look at the nuts, bolts, and screws in his stomach. I wonder if he ever gets stomach aches?"

"Hi," the voice of the robot said. "I am Mechanical Max. Who are you?"

Phillip was almost too excited to answer. "This is Joseph and I'm Phillip. I've waited a long time to meet you. I like to make and fix mechanical toys, but I have never seen anything like you before."

"I work from a computer," said the robot. "Watch my metal coils flash as I speak."

The mechanical man seemed to like
Phillip. He began to follow him around
the Space Center. All the children
laughed when they saw Max wobbling
along behind Phillip.

The children took turns asking Max
questions. When they pushed his
buttons, Max replied in his funny
mechanical voice.

At last it was time to leave. The kids enjoyed visiting the Space Center. Everyone was sorry to say good-bye to Max. The class thanked him and waved as they got back on the bus.

With a big yawn, Phillip slumped down on the seat next to Joseph. After a while, Phillip had the feeling there was someone sitting behind him. When he turned around, he found it hard not to yell out loud. It was Max, the mechanical man!

"What are you doing here?" whispered
Phillip.

"I like you," replied Max, flashing his
coils on and off. "Besides, I need a
mechanic to put my nephew, Chaos,
back together. You are good at making
and fixing mechanical toys. You'll have
no problem making Chaos as good
as new."

"What happened to him?" asked
Phillip.

"Chaos used to be the chef at the Space Center lunchroom," said Max. "But he spoiled too many meals. So he was disconnected. Now he is a mass of machinery in a storage closet."

"Poor Chaos," said Phillip.

"I was sure you could help me," said Max. "After you have fixed Chaos, the three of us can go to Chicago. That's where the rest of my family lives. You will come in handy if anyone in my family has mechanical problems."

"But I don't want to go to Chicago!" Phillip cried. "I want to stay here with my own family. I won't go! I WON'T GO!"

"You won't go where?" asked Joseph. "You fell asleep soon after we got on the bus. We're back at school now, and the only place you're going is inside."

"THANK GOODNESS!" said Phillip, rubbing his eyes.

silent w

write	wrote	wrap	wrapper
wrist	wring	wrong	wreck
wren	wrinkle	wrench	writer

silent k

knot	knob	knee	kneel
knit	knitted	know	known
knew	knock	knocking	knife
knead	knuckle	knowledge	knapsack

We're Off to See the Wizard

Scarecrow was stuffed full of straw from head to toe. He spent each day perched on a pole to scare the crows away. What Scarecrow wanted most in the world was to have a brain. So imagine the joy he felt when Dorothy told him that she was going to see the wizard. The wizard could do wonderful things—even give Scarecrow a brain.

Dorothy and Scarecrow started down the yellow brick road, singing . . .

We're off to see the wizard
The wonderful wizard of Oz.
We hear he is a whiz of a whiz
If ever a whiz there was.
If ever, oh ever, a whiz there was,
The wizard of Oz
Is one because,
Because, because, because, because, because,
Because of the wonderful things he does!
We're off to see the wizard
The wonderful wizard of Oz.

But what Scarecrow didn't know was
that he had a brain and had been using
it all the time!

Use Your Brain

Knock on your head with your knuckles. Knock on the top. Knock on the back. Knock on your forehead. Can you hear the hollow sound? Your head may sound hollow, but it is not empty. Your brain is inside.

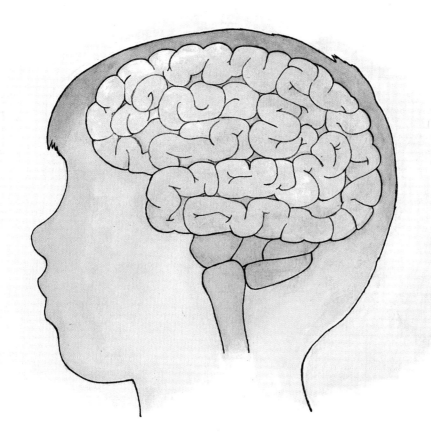

Your brain is soft and gray and
wrinkled. It is made up of thousands of
tiny parts called *cells*. The cells are tied
to one another by tiny, thin strands
called *nerves*. There are nerves in every
part of your body except in your
fingernails and your hair. That is why
it does not hurt when you cut your nails
or get a haircut. They have no nerves to
send messages to your brain.

Nerves are like telephone wires. They carry messages to and from the brain. This is how your brain keeps in touch with every part of you.

Nerves carry messages **to** your brain from your eyes, ears, nose, mouth, and skin. The brain gets these messages and tells you what is going on in the world around you.

This is an example of how it happens. A fire truck sounds its siren. The noise comes into your ear. The nerves in your ear send messages to your brain. This is how you know a fire truck is passing by outside.

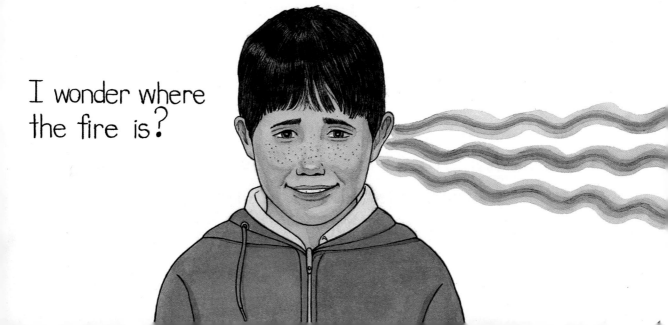

I wonder where the fire is?

Nerves also carry messages **from** your brain out to your body. Suppose you think you are going to miss the bus. You know you must hurry. Your brain sends a message to your legs—your knees bend and you start to run.

When you finish reading this page, your brain will send a message to your hand, wrist, and arm. It will work quicker than a wink. You won't even notice. You will simply decide it's time to turn the page—and you will turn it.

Your brain is very important. It is protected by a thick, hard bone all around it, called the *skull*. Your brain floats in a liquid that acts like a cushion. It keeps your brain from being bruised when you turn a somersault.

Sometimes your brain gets tired and does not work well. It slows down and gets its messages mixed up. Then things go wrong for you. You forget. You make mistakes. You can't pay attention—even to television. When your brain is tired, you get sleepy. Your brain is telling you it wants a rest. It is time to take your brain to bed.

But most of the time your brain works well. It takes in messages quick as a flash. It sends out messages just as fast. Then things go well and you feel fine.

Your brain does so many things. It stores all the knowledge you have picked up. It helps you remember things. It helps you remember the alphabet and how to write letters. It helps you remember your best friend's face and the taste of your favorite ice cream.

Your brain helps you do new things, too. It helps you turn cartwheels, ride a bike, swim, knit, tie a knot, and wrap a gift.

With the help of your brain, you are even reading the words on this page.

Maybe someday your brain will help you drive a car, write a book, or even fly a jet!

Krin's Story

Krin was excited! A well-known author was visiting his school today!

Krin went into the auditorium with his classmates and sat down.

The author came in. He went up on stage and stood behind the microphone. He was a very tall, thin man. "Students ask me how to become a writer," he began. "This is what I tell them."

"First, you must have a knowledge of
many things in the world. Try to see,
hear, and feel everything around you.
That way you can write an interesting
story."

Krin looked around the auditorium.
He could hear the tap-tap of boots on
the floor as a latecomer tried to find a
seat. He could feel the softness of his

knitted wool vest. Nearby he could see
Mrs. Chrisman, his homeroom teacher,
with her curly red hair. He could smell
her sweet perfume. It reminded him of
orange blossoms.

"Let's try a game," said the author.
"Raise your hand and tell me how to
write about the sea. There are no wrong
answers, so don't be afraid."

A few students started whispering.
Other students seemed to be thinking,
but not a single hand went up.

Krin imagined himself on the deck of a proud ship. The sea was a beautiful deep green. It seemed so real to Krin. He had a knot in his stomach, but he raised his hand.

The author pointed to Krin. "What is your name?" he asked.

"Krin."

"Well, Krin, tell us what you are writing in your mind."

"I am on the deck of a ship," said
Krin. "The sea is all around me. I can
smell the salty air. I can hear the
gentle knocking of the waves against the
sides of the ship. I can hear the ship
creaking as we go along. The sun is
sparkling on the water. And way up in
the blue sky is a little white cloud all
by itself. In the distance I can see a
sandy beach where we will drop anchor."

"I can really feel and see what you described," said the author.

But Krin was so wrapped up in his story that he did not hear the author.

"Krin?" said the author. Krin snapped back to attention.

"Sorry," he said, in a small, quiet voice. "It's so much fun thinking about the sea that I started to daydream."

The author laughed. "I do that when I am writing, too. With your imagination, Krin, you will be a good writer someday. Now, can someone tell me how to write about the jungle?"

Krin smiled. He could see a huge elephant in a deep, dark jungle. The elephant was gray and wrinkled and had a long trunk. Krin drifted off on another daydream.

PHONICS CHART
Sound/Symbol Relationship Sequence

Starting Out, A

/a/aA (ant)
/n/nN (nest)
/r/rR (run)
/d/dD (dog)
/u/uU (up)
/m/mM (map)

/p/pP (pin)
/i/iI (in)
/s/sS (sun)
/o/oO (on)
/t/tT (ten)
/e/eE (egg)

/g/gG (game)
/k/cC (can)
/h/hH (hat)
/f/fF (fan)

Exploring, B

ar (art)
–er (farmer, runner)
–ed (ended, farmed, dropped)
/w/wW (win, warm, swan)
aw (saw)
ow (cow)
/l/lL, ll (let, all)

/b/bB (bed)
–le (apple)
/k/kK (kitten)
/k/ck (sack)
nk (bank)
/ā/a_e (made)
are (care)
/ē/e, ee (we, see)
/ē/ea (eat)

/ā/ai (rain)
/ī/i, i_e, ie (find, nine, pie)
ir (bird)
/ō/o, o_e (go, note)
or, ore (for, more)
/ō/oa, oe (coat, toe)
/j/jJ (jam)
/v/vV (vote)

Reaching Higher, C

sh (she)
ch, –tch (chin, catch)
th (then)
wh (what)
qu (queen)
xX (box)
yY (yes)
zZ (zip)
–ng (song)
–ing (jumping, sailing, winning, smiling)

–ed (handed, needed, stopped, waved)
–er (other, longer, baker, swimmer)
ir, ar, or, ur (girl, dollar, work, fur)
/ā/–ay (day)
/ī/–y (my)
/ē/–y, –ey (happy, key)
/lē/–ly (safely)
soft c (cent, circus, fancy)

soft g (germ, giant, stingy)
–dge (edge)
–sion, –tion (admission, decision, motion)
short oo (book)
long oo (moon)
ow (slow)
ou (out, four, soup, your, young)
u, u_e (music, rule)
ue, ui (blue, suit)

continued on next page

Jumping Up, D

Formal review of
  sound/symbols in
  Texts, A,B,C
oi, oy (oil, boy)

ew, eau (few, beauty)
aw, au (saw, pause)
ph (photo)
gh (laugh)

ch (echo, machine)
silent w (write)
silent k (knit)

Rolling Along, E

silent b, l (comb,
  talk)
silent g, h, gh (sign,
  hour, right)
ea (head, great)
ear (earn, bear,
  heart)

/ē/ie, ei (field, ceiling)
/ā/ei, eigh, ey (vein,
  eight, they)
ough (rough, cough,
  bought, though,
  bough, through)
/i/y (myth)

/ī/uy, ui (buy, guide)
/i/ui (build)
/ə/ai (captain)
/e/ue (guess)
/əl/ile (missile)
silent t (listen)
silent n (autumn)